WHY *POWERFUL PLANTS*?

So how can parents who care about their child's connection to plants, nature, and the well-being of planet earth find common ground to get their kids outside and interested in the very things that feed us and keep our world healthy and livable? *Powerful Plants* was developed to create a bridge for kids between entertainment and technology and plants, nature, and the environment — the "real" world.

Unlike other popular fantasy characters, our plant superheroes don't "battle" each other. Instead they work together to help save the planet from destructive human villains. The "Selfish Seven", including their dastardly ringleader Grendal Greed and sidekicks like Frackin' Frank and Wasteful Wally, seem to be only thinking about themselves.

Too often these days, learning, exploring, and creating take a back seat to more passive forms of engagement like TV and video games. Here at *Powerful Plants* we aim to help foster a reconnection with nature by "edutaining" children. They'll be learning incredibly useful information about plants, nature, and the health of our planet without even realizing it! We must warn you, however — many parents have been known to become quite obsessed with our characters and stories!

Powerful Plants is a story with an endearing cast of characters that are sure to win the hearts and minds of most any 5- to 12-year-old child (and, to be honest, quite a few adults too!).

Heirloom Seeds... Just for Kids

We now sell a complete line of easy-to-grow heirloom vegetable seeds, herbs, and flowers just for kids. When viewed through a phone or tablet with our free app, each character on the seed pack comes to life to share planting instructions and more! Available at your local independent garden center, gift shop, or online at PowerfulPlants.net .

BRING THE PLANTS TO LIFE WITH A PHONE OR TABLET
DOWNLOAD THE FREE COMPANION APP AT PowerfulPlants.net

WHAT IS POWERFUL PLANTS EXACTLY?

Powerful Plants books, seeds, and contests are no ordinary forms of entertainment. Our concept is to provide a multi-faceted learning or "edu-tainment" experience for children. The goal is to foster an interest in plants and our environment. The end result is a form of entertainment that makes it easy and fun for kids to want to spend more time outdoors.

In our interactive books, a child first reads the written portion of each chapter, and then answers three questions by using our free app on a phone or tablet. This ensures reading comprehension and information retention. Once the questions are answered, the character is viewed through the phone or tablet. Each character then comes to life as a talking, animated personality right on the page (so do our characters on our seed packs). The child's answers are also captured, and points toward our grand prize contest awarded for each correct answer.

OUR WEBSITE

PowerfulPlants.net offers several FREE contests that allow kids to create, contribute, and compete by designing new characters, growing a vegetable patch, or even recording their own version of our theme song! There are also points awarded for photos taken with the real-life versions of the various characters.

At stake are lots of great prizes, like CSA memberships for local, organic produce and family vacations at an organic farm in Pennsylvania — www.OldSchoolFarm.com. All this while learning and having FUN!

When children get their hands in the soil, they are much more likely to eat and enjoy the food they help grow.

The wood-fired earthen oven at Old School Farm

Dedication:
For my sons, Owen and Coleman Benner, who have provided inspiration, creative ideas, and unwavering support for this venture. May your fascination with nature, positive energy, and zest for life remain with you always. All my love – "Daddy" and "Coach"

Special thanks to Onisor Sorin Ion from Romania, who, on a whim, decided to team up with me as the illustrator of our characters. Sorin – your artistic talent and unwavering belief in the concept have been a true inspiration and driving force since inception. Thank you.

Al Benner – Creator and Author

POWERFUL PLANTS VOLUME 1 – *THE CARROT-NAPPING*

Text & Illustrations Copyright 2014 by Powerful Plants LLC
All rights reserved

This book was typeset in Century Schoolbook

Published by Powerful Plants LLC
303 Upper Woods Road
Honesdale, PA 18431 USA

info@PowerfulPlants.net
PowerfulPlants.net

Contents

Weeping Willow
Salix babylonica

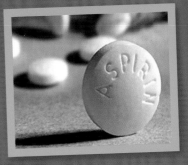

The main ingredient in aspirin is also found in willow bark.

Weeping Willows are easy to identify by their shape.

Are you in pain? Gosh, I hope not. I am often sad because I can't stop thinking about others who are hurting. I want to help them. Sometimes I give them my twigs to chew on. Did you know that the main ingredient in aspirin (salicylic acid) is also found in my bark?

I am originally from China and was brought here a long time ago on a sail ship by people who admired my weeping branches and the way I am able to soak up water and grow in wet areas.

For thousands of years, willow twigs have been used for basket making.

Through time I have been used for weaving baskets, and long ago people believed I had magical powers — they even said witches made brooms from my twigs. You don't believe in witches, do you?

I have some other very important and interesting information to share with you, but first I need to know if you are serious about helping me on a special mission to heal our planet.

If so, download the free app at PowerfulPlants.net. Then tap on the Powerful Plants icon and point your phone or tablet at Weeping Willow to answer three questions and then bring her to life.

Witch's brooms were thought to have been made from willow twigs.

Douglas Fir
Pseudotsuga menziesii

Hello from the great Northwest, youngsters. My name is Douglas Fir, and I have been hanging around these western mountains and the Pacific coastline for hundreds of years. Sometimes it gets kind of boring with nothing to do but watch squirrels or owls on my branches or inside my trunk!

Long ago some Indian tribes used my sap for sealing their leather water jugs. Now we firs are more likely to be cut for timber. Flooring is a common use of our wood. I can grow very tall and have reached heights of 300 feet — that's the length of a football field! I've been around a long, long time, surviving the clear-cutting for lumber from a hundred years ago.

With every generation of "modern" humans, there always seem to be a few greedy ones who will stop at nothing to make money, even if it means cutting down a whole forest.

Some of the cutting has stopped, as the leader of the Selfish Seven, Grendal Greed, has moved on to other projects where he can make even more money. But now we old trees face other challenges like global warming, pollution, and insect pests brought over by humans from other parts of the world.

Now tap on the Powerful Plants icon and point your phone or tablet at Douglas Fir to answer three questions and bring him to life. Download the free app at PowerfulPlants.net.

Douglas Fir trees have been found that are 1,300 years old!

Sadly, back in the old days most of these giants were cut for timber.

Douglas Fir is one of the best woods for flooring material.

Doll's Eye
Actaea pachypoda

Doll's Eye berries are highly poisonous to humans & animals (not birds)

A shade-loving plant, Doll's Eye has beautiful spring flowers.

I certainly am a very powerful plant. I'll tell you why in a moment. One of my most important jobs is to keep an eye on the forest. Because I have lots of eyes, this is easy for me. Except when my eyes (actually berries) fall off in late fall!

As winter approaches I begin to die back and move all my energy into my roots and go to sleep for the winter. I become invisible, as all my leaves, berries, and stems dry up and fall off when it goes below freezing.

I have a cousin whose leaves and flowers also look like mine, but he has berries that turn dark red in the fall.

To learn more, point your phone or tablet at Doll's Eye, then answer three questions to bring her to life.
Download the free app at PowerfulPlants.net.

Doll's Eye is an attractive woodland wildflower.

13

Elder Berry
Sambucus Canadensis

Ripe Elderberries have many uses — jam, syrup, wine & healing tonics.

Hi there, young whippersnapper! I was getting a bit lonely here with my bottle of elderberry tonic and nobody to talk with, so I'm glad that you have dropped by.

I'm an old-timer. Just when I think my time here on Earth is over, I send out new shoots underground and keep expanding myself. I just can't seem to call it quits!

Birds often stop by and eat my berries — when they fly away, they leave my seeds behind. I have long-lost cousins all over the place! If you have a farm, be sure to plant me, as chickens and turkeys love to sit beneath my branches and eat my berries as they fall.

I've seen a lot of changes in the world. Back in the old days, juice from my berries was used for all kinds of things, like wine and special healing drinks that helped cure sick people. Lucky for me, some folks have recently decided to start growing more of my kind for just these reasons. But be careful: don't eat my leaves, stems, or roots — they contain a poison — cyanide.

Now I'm going to let you in on a secret many people don't know much about. It involves a very dangerous man who has been seen a lot lately in states like Pennsylvania, Ohio, Wyoming, and Texas.

To learn more, get the free app at PowerfulPlants.net. *Then tap on the Powerful Plants icon and point your phone or tablet at Elder Berry to answer three questions and bring him to life.*

A "winter tonic" made from boiled, ripe elderberries.

Daucus

Daucus carota

Hi, kids! I'm Daucus — your silly and goofy vegetable pal. My friends like to tease me because they think I can never be serious. I'm always playing jokes on everyone. I can't resist — it's just too much fun! When my good friend Toma Tillo or his relatives the tomatoes start to blush and turn different colors, it is probably because I have just embarrassed them again!

One thing I know for sure is that my name is very old. Daucus is the Latin name for the carrot family. My relatives are Cel Ery, Par Snip, Florence Fennel, and the herbs, Dill and Cori Ander. Ah, the herbs; boy, are they a real pain in my butt — always complaining about something! Talk about high-maintenance plants!

Did you know that my distant relative Poison Hemlock is quite a dangerous guy? This nasty fella packs a mean punch in his root. The famous Greek philosopher Socrates was most likely poisoned by a deadly brew made from the root of Poison Hemlock.

Carrots come in many colors — the first were thought to be purple.

But now back to ME! When it comes to good taste, health, and special powers, I have it ALL, kiddos! Are you interested in seeing a little better at night? Some studies show that I can help your night vision.

Want lots of Vitamin A and other important minerals? How about that sweet crunch? Nothing can beat me for a tasty and healthy snack. Just don't "double dip" me in that hummus!

Hey, it seems like someone has snuck into the carrot patch. I'm going to need you to aim your phone or tablet at the carrot patch now and answer three questions to help me find out what is going on....

Poison Hemlock — a relative of the carrot family.

Better night vision? The beta-carotene in carrots promotes healthy eyes.

Carrots are full of beta-carotene that our bodies convert to Vitamin A.

Sphag Num – Spooky Secrets
Sphagnum moss (120 species)

Sphagnum moss can hold twenty times its weight in water!

Hi there. Our name is Sphag Num and we have many special powers.

For thousands of years our relatives have died over and over on top of each other, and in the process they have created huge deposits of peat moss. Peat moss, as you may know, is often used in potting soil mixes to start seedlings.

We've also been used on battlefields for a long time to keep wounds from becoming infected. We've even been used by many Indian tribes as an absorbent liner for natural diapers.

Because we prevent rot and fungus and absorb lots of moisture, we are also used around plant roots when they are being shipped from one place to another. We keep them from drying out and from rotting.

We do also hide some spooky secrets from the past. Now, hundreds (or even thousands) of years later, harvesters of peat moss sometimes find some pretty amazing things in our bogs. The high acid content of peat moss, the low oxygen levels, and the cold temperatures do a good job of preserving most anything.

To learn more, point your phone or tablet at Sphag Num, then answer three questions to bring them to life. Download the free app at PowerfulPlants.net.

Sphagnum bogs can be thousands of years old .

For keeping seedlings healthy, nothing beats peat moss.

Peat moss being harvested

The Carrot-Napping

Daucus has been taken hostage and driven hundreds of miles away to a secret underground laboratory that is run by Mean Gene — a scientist who is paid by Grendal Greed to do genetic research on different fruits; vegetables; fish; and, soon, even farm animals.

This is done so these plants and animals can be changed to produce more food, which means more profits for Grendal and his investors.

A few years ago, Mean Gene came up with Chem Safe — a chemical farmers now spray on their fields of Soy Bean and Field Corn, two Powerful Plants characters. This is done to kill any weeds that try to come up. The corn and soybean plants have been changed in the lab in such a way they are not harmed by the Chem Safe spray.

Nobody knows what eating plants that have been changed in this way and sprayed will do to humans or animals over long periods of time. Some studies show it can make animals and humans sick.

Grendal Greed and his wealthy friends were somehow able to convince the people in our government who are in charge of keeping the food supply safe to allow these seeds to be sold to farmers.

Some farmers like this "GMO" seed and the chemical spray that goes with it because they think it saves them time and money. One of the Selfish Seven, Lazy Larry, is always out talking with farmers about how great Chem Safe is and how much easier it will make their lives.

To find out what happens to Daucus, point your phone or tablet at him, then answer three questions. The free app can be downloaded at PowerfulPlants.net.

Poison Ivy
Toxicodendron radicans

Poison Ivy has three leaves and they are shiny with oil.

Pretty yet sinister, clever but cunning, Poison Ivy is one of those Powerful Plants that can change her mood quickly. She can change from a small, seemingly harmless plant into a nasty villain for little or no reason.

Over time she can slowly smother, strangle, and choke out a perfectly healthy tree. She can also cause humans to scratch what soon become oozing blisters. Anyone meeting with Poison Ivy must be extremely cautious.

She is, however, a friend to certain birds in late fall and winter, when they enjoy dining on her white berries.

In addition to causing a skin rash on 80 percent of humans because of the toxic oil on her leaves, she can also grab onto most any surface with thousands of little hair-like feet that grip very strongly.

Poison Ivy has strong powers, and she has been known to use them the wrong way. She has a history of being a "double agent" — working for two sides at once.

She is definitely not someone to be trusted, but because of her powers and intelligence she could perhaps be helpful someday in defeating the Selfish Seven.

To learn more, point your phone or tablet at Poison Ivy, then answer three questions to bring her to life.

Berries turn white and are food for birds

Trees are a favorite of Poison Ivy. Her hair-like feet grip to the trunk.

Jack in the Pulpit
Arisaema triphyllum

Jacks come up each spring, and die back in winter. They can live for 100 years!

Doll's Eye sees with all her eyes what is going on in the forest, but unlike a camera, she can see in all directions at once!

For hearing everything that goes on in the forest, the Powerful Plants team depends on Jack in the Pulpit.

Jack is surrounded by a hood (pulpit) that he uses to catch sound waves and then direct them to his thin body. His body works like a sound-absorbing microphone.

Jack can easily be grown from seed and is found in most any moist, shady area. For this reason, Jack can easily be seeded along streams or in other shaded forest areas, and is very useful for listening in on the conversations of others.

Having a lot of Jack in the Pulpits not only makes the forest floor nice to look at, but also helps protect the forest from those that might try to harm these fragile habitats.

Plans are being made to have Doll's Eye work more closely with Jack in the Pulpit so together they can be the "eyes and ears" of the forest.

To learn more, point your phone or tablet at Jack in the Pulpit, then answer three questions to bring him to life. Download the free app at PowerfulPlants.net.

The berries turn red in fall and have 3-5 seeds inside.

Jacks sprout up from a small bulb each spring

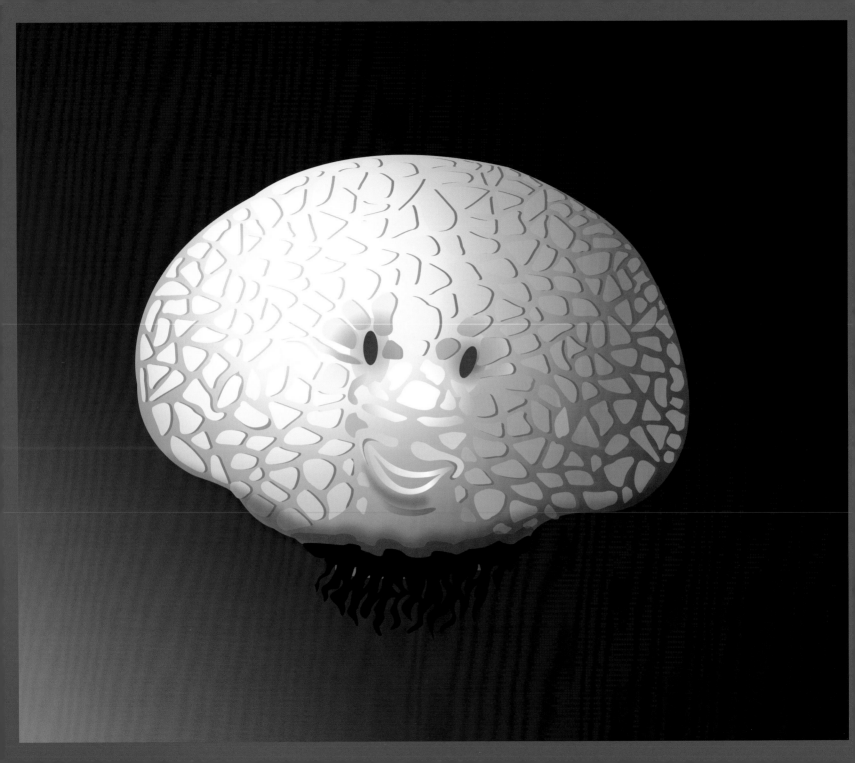

Puff Ball
Lycoperdon perlatum

One Giant Puffball (Calvatia gigantean) can contain up to 7 trillion spores!

Puffballs are delicious sautéed, but be sure to have an expert identify them, or any wild mushroom before eating.

Somehow the word gets out through the Powerful Plants network that Daucus was in trouble. In fact, as soon as he is taken away by Grendal Greed's tough guy, plants all over the world communicate with each other about this horrible "carrot-napping".

It is late fall, and one Powerful Plant who is getting near the end of his life is watching this very closely.

His name is Puff Ball. Not only is he a wild mushroom that humans can eat, he is also a guy you don't want to upset. Daucus is one of his good friends, and Puff Ball has become very angry because he was taken away. Puff Ball has a neat trick he can do if the timing is right, and late fall is the right time.

When puffballs dry out you can stomp on them, making a cloud of spores!

Soon you will learn all about how he can huff and puff and then do something pretty amazing.

To learn more, point your phone or tablet at Puff Ball, then answer three questions to bring him to life. Download the free app at PowerfulPlants.net.

Muscle Wood

Carpinus caroliniana

The rippling, muscle-like appearance of "Musclewood"

Puff Ball is not the only Powerful Plant unhappy with Daucus being taken to a secret underground lab.

Another strong tree character has been flexing his muscles ever since he learned the news.

Muscle Wood is a medium-sized tree with rippling muscle-like branches and a twisty trunk. He is incredibly strong and is often called upon for help when strength is needed. Puff Ball asked Muscle Wood if he would go with him to rescue Daucus. Let's check in now to see what Muscle Wood thinks of all this….

To learn more, point your phone or tablet at Muscle Wood, then answer three questions to bring him to life. Download the free app at PowerfulPlants.net.

Uses: Tool handles and firewood

The small "nutlets" are food for wildlife.

Musclewood can sometimes have a twisty, curvy trunk.

Puff Ball and Muscle Wood Try to Rescue Daucus

Muscle Wood and Puff Ball arrive at the creepy cave entrance. All the Witch's Hairs stare down at them from the trees above. They whisper to each other in a strange language that even Puff Ball has trouble understanding.

Puff Ball and Darryl lower Muscle Wood down to the ground and open the digger spade.

Muscle Wood has been given special powers on this day by Mother Nature. These powers will allow him and Puff Ball to move themselves along and into the cave.

By this time it is almost dark, and Puff Ball takes out a special light he brought for the trip. The light shows any footprints on the ground and helps them go the right way. Without the light it would be easy to get lost because there are so many different tunnels that branch off inside the cave.

Finally, after following the footprint trail for about ten minutes, the two plant friends come upon a large door made of reinforced steel. The thick and heavy door is closed and locked.

To find out what happens next, point your phone or tablet at the scene image, then answer three questions. Download the free app at PowerfulPlants.net.

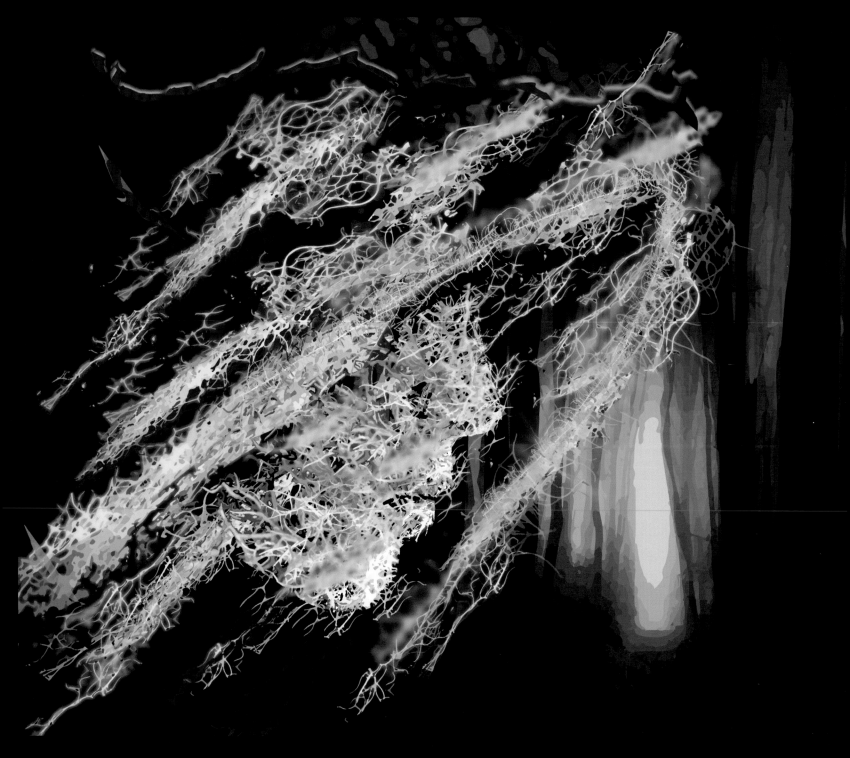

The Secret Life of Witch's Hair
Alectoria sarmentosa

Witch's hair is an "epiphyte" — it has no roots and requires no soil.

Witch's Hair (also called Old Man's Beard) doesn't look much like a plant. That's because it is a special kind of plant called "lichen".

Lichens don't have roots, and they don't need soil to grow. All they need is something to hang on to. Usually this is a rock or a tree.

This plant is useful for many things. When dry, it makes a great fire starter. Witch's Hair is also used by birds for nest-building, and if it ever does fall to the ground, this lichen becomes fertilizer for the tree.

Lichens are also used to make perfumes and dyes, and are a food for deer and elk in winter. Witch's Hair is usually found growing in areas that are damp and humid most of the year.

It is a plant that is known to grow best in areas with low levels of pollution. If you see a lot of these lichens then you know you are breathing clean air.

Witch's Hair was a big reason Daucus was saved from the juicer, so let's see if we can find out a little more about this strange and mysterious Powerful Plants character.

To learn more, point your phone or tablet at Witch's Hair, then answer three questions to bring her to life.

Lichens cling to trees, but do not harm them in any way.

Douglas Fir - a wise old tree

Hi again, people and plants – Douglas Fir here. At this time we would like to bring you a special update on the story of Poison Ivy and her evil ways.

What we know now is this: Poison Ivy has been working with one of the Selfish Seven, climate change princes, Warming Wanda.

Global warming really helps Poison Ivy. Certain plants grow much better with high levels of carbon dioxide in the air. Poison Ivy is one of them.

Due to the warming of the planet and the big increase in carbon dioxide over the past 50 years, Poison Ivy has been able to double the amount of area she covers. For this reason, she wants Warming Wanda to continue to do whatever she can to keep increasing global warming.

As you may know, plants use carbon dioxide (CO_2) they absorb from the air to grow. In return, they give off oxygen (O_2) - what we humans and other animals need to breathe. There is now more CO_2 in our atmosphere than there has been for thousands of yeare.

To learn more, point your phone or tablet at Douglas Fir, then answer three questions to bring him to life. Download the free app at PowerfulPlants.net.

A mature Douglas Fir can grow to be 300 feet tall!

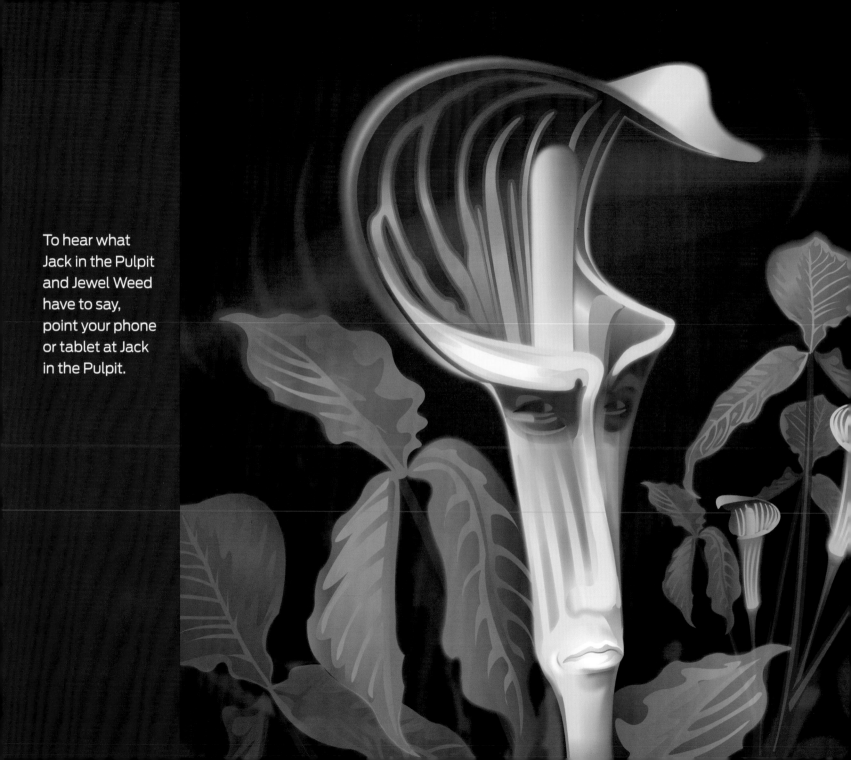

To hear what Jack in the Pulpit and Jewel Weed have to say, point your phone or tablet at Jack in the Pulpit.

Jewel Weed protects humans from Poison Ivy and also provides fun and games for children

To bring Daucus to life and learn more of his story, point your phone or tablet at him and then answer three questions.

Get Outside!

The great outdoors and/or a vegetable garden are full of amazing sights, smells, and tastes for kids. The learning and connectedness to place that occur are unsurpassed.

Visit PowerfulPlants. net today to learn all about our exciting contests that get kids outside, their hands in the soil, competing for some pretty amazing prizes.

Look up. Look down. Look around. There's power all around you; it's up to you to use it now!

To hear more from Weeping Willow, Jack in the Pulpit, and Elder Berry, please point your phone or tablet at this image to bring them to life. Download the free app at PowerfulPlants.net

We may think we know what kids like, but we don't take too many chances... The author's twin boys and their schoolmates make a terrific "brain trust" when it comes to helping design characters, select voice talent, and even share a story idea or two when Dad gets writer's block!

Plain and simple: when children grow up around plants and have the opportunity to nurture and enjoy food from their own garden, most seem to develop healthy eating habits.

By getting kids more involved with plants so they better understand them, we are all doing the world a big service.

Cities offer many opportunities for visual beautification and growing food. From abandoned lots to rooftop gardens to that narrow backyard, there are endless ways to get children engaged with their food and plants.

Photo Credits

Book

All photos of Doll's Eye, page 13 by Meneerke bloem (Own work) [GFDL (http://www.gnu.org/copyleft/fdl.html) or CC-BY-SA-3.0-2.5-2.0-1.0 (http://creativecommons.org/licenses/by-sa/3.0)], via Wikimedia Commons

Elderberry plant photo, page 15 by Jonathan Billinger http://www.willowherb.co.uk/

Night Vision photo, page 19 by Rob Shenk

Sphagnum bog photo (top right), page 21 by Walter Baxter http://www.geograph.org.uk/profile/6638 (also used in animated scene)

Seedling photo, page 21 by "Bff" http://commons.wikimedia.org/wiki/User:Bff

Peat harvesting photo, page 21 by "Abugar" – Wikimedia commons

Poison Ivy berries, page 23 by Sam Fraser-Smith https://www.flickr.com/people/8379434@N07

Giant Puffball in pasture, page 29 by Hans Hillewaert http://commons.wikimedia.org/wiki/User:Biopics

Puffballs ready to disperse spores, page 29 by David Lochlin https://www.flickr.com/people/74747209@N05

Puffball main photo, page 29 by Sandy Rae

Musclewood main photo and Musclewood Nutlets, page 31 by Richard Webb, Bugwood.org, USA

Witch's Hair - both photos, page 33 by Jason Hollinger

Photos in animated scenes

Weeping Willow scene –
Nighttime pollution photo by Gavin Shaefer
Polluted lake photo by "Wilfredor" http://commons.wikimedia.org/wiki/User:Wilfredor

Elder Berry scene –
Fracking operation photo by Joshua Doubek (Own work) [CC-BY-SA-3.0 (http://creativecommons.org/licenses/by-sa/3.0)], via Wikimedia Commons

Daucus scene -
Cracked ground image by Jeroen Moes from Florence, Italy (Ground | Orange) [CC-BY-SA-2.0 (http://creativecommons.org/licenses/by-sa/2.0)], via Wikimedia Commons

Farm photo taken at Eliot Coleman's Four Season Farm in Brooksville, Maine. Photo by Al Benner

Sphag Num scene –
Iceberg photo by Kim Hansen (Own work (Own photo)) [GFDL (http://www.gnu.org/copyleft/fdl.html) or CC-BY-SA-3.0-2.5-2.0-1.0 (http://creativecommons.org/licenses/by-sa/3.0)], via Wikimedia Commons

Peat harvesting photo by markjhandel (Peat Bog) [CC-BY-2.0 (http://creativecommons.org/licenses/by/2.0)], via Wikimedia Commons

Musclewood Scene -
Tree Digger: Dutchman Industries [GFDL (http://www.gnu.org/copyleft/fdl.html) or CC-BY-SA-3.0 (http://creativecommons.org/licenses/by-sa/3.0/)], via Wikimedia Commons

Poison Ivy Scene -
Large poison ivy vine/bush - By Jaknouse (Own work) [GFDL (http://www.gnu.org/copyleft/fdl.html), CC-BY-SA-3.0 (http://creativecommons.org/licenses/by-sa/3.0/) or FAL], via Wikimedia Commons

Four Exciting Contests & Great Prizes!

Photos with Characters

Kids earn Power Points to be used toward our grand prize contest by having their photo taken with any of the *Powerful Plants* characters from the book, website, or seed packs.

Design a Character

Children design our next character and the artwork is posted on our website for visitors to vote on. Every three months the top three designs receive prizes, recognition on our site, and points toward our grand prize contest. The top design will be used by our artist, Sorin, in designing our next character.

Grow Carrots

Children plant and nurture the carrot seeds included with this book. Daucus, the lovable carrot character, comes to life to share planting tips right on the seed pack using our free app for your phone or tablet. Details on PowerfulPlants. net.

Record a Music Video

This contest is decided by popular vote every three months on our website. First, kids listen to the Powerful Plants theme song. Next, they download the background soundtrack and lyrics. Finally, kids perform their own version of the catchy tune and upload the recording to the site. Prizes and points for the top three vote-getters.

Grand Prize Contest

Each December 21st (winter solstice), we award two children (by age bracket) with the highest total points from all contests as grand prize winners with a four-day Farm Getaway for their family at our 50-acre organic farm in northeastern Pennsylvania.

Heirloom Carrot Seed!

Be sure to visit PowerfulPlants.net for details about our carrot-growing competition and all our fun contests and great prizes! When viewed with a phone or tablet using our free app, Daucus, our endearing carrot character, also comes to life right on the seed packet to share planting instructions and more!

WHY THIS BOOK?

Powerful Plants creator and author, Al Benner was exposed to plants and nature from a young age. His father, Dave, a professor of Ornamental Horticulture, was always sharing with Al his knowledge and love of plants.

In turn, Al feels it is his responsibility to ensure his 8-year-old twin boys, Owen and Coleman, are exposed to all the magic plants offer us.

We live in a time when children often grow up isolated from nature. Powerful Plants stories and characters reconnect kids with plants and the natural world while also conveying the importance of protecting our fragile planet.

The idea is to "edutain", creating a bridge between useful information, technology, and the outdoors in a fun, kid-friendly way.

HOW DID POWERFUL PLANTS COME ABOUT?

Al Benner, the founder of Powerful Plants, is not only passionate about plants, he is also the father of twin 8-year-old boys. Al believes being a kid should be about one thing — having fun. If it isn't fun and entertaining, a kid isn't interested for long.

It's what that "fun" is, however, that can be critically important to the development of children and how they perceive the world around them. For Al, seeing his boys spending countless hours with popular fantasy trading cards was getting old. He longed for something more — something where kids could be entertained, yet at the same time be learning real, interesting facts and information.

47